SHORT ROMANTIC PIECES F

Edited by LIONEL SALTER

BOOK II

The pieces in this book are about Grades 3 and 4 in standard (Associated Board)
Metronome marks within square brackets are editorial

THE ASSOCIATED BOARD OF THE ROYAL SCHOOLS OF MUSIC

STUDY in G

LEMOINE, Op.37 No.27

Shortly after the turn of the 18th century Henry Lemoine was one of the most sought-after piano teachers in Paris: in the ensuing years he wrote a piano method, a harmony textbook, and a large number of small piano pieces. In 1817 he inherited the music publishing firm that his father had founded. The *Etudes enfantines* from which this polka-like piece is taken appeared in 1841.

MAZURKA

GLINKA

In his youth Glinka took piano lessons from John Field in St Petersburg. Possessed of private means, he travelled extensively in Europe, but largely as a result of his operas *A life for the Tsar* and *Ruslan and Lyudmila* he is regarded as the founder of the Russian nationalist school of composers. This Mazurka has a curious resemblance to Chopin's Mazurka in A minor, Op.17 No.4.

INNOCENCE

Moderato [♩ = 108]

BURGMÜLLER, Op.100 No.5

Johann Friedrich is the only member of the Burgmüller family of musicians who is remembered today; but his father was one of the founders of the Lower Rhine Festival, and Schumann declared that the early death (at the age of 26) of his younger brother Norbert was the greatest blow since that of Schubert. Johann himself settled in Paris, where he became a popular figure.

AB 1899

FOLKSONG

SCHUMANN, Op.68 No.9

Schumann wrote the *Album for the young,* from which this comes, primarily for his eldest child's seventh birthday: he enjoyed the task so much that he composed all the pieces – more than the 43 eventually published – in just over a fortnight.

STUDY in A flat

Andante ♩ = 54

HELLER, Op.47 No.23

Born in Pest, the Hungarian capital, Heller studied in Vienna and Augsburg but settled in Paris, where some critics considered him an even more poetical pianist than Chopin. Many of his numerous Etudes, including his Op.47, were designed to further the development of expressive playing.

AB 1899

RIGAUDON

ALKAN, Op.63 No.27

On account of his many large-scale virtuoso keyboard works Alkan (real name Morhange) has been called 'the Berlioz of the piano'. He was so precocious that he was admitted to the Paris Conservatoire at the age of 6: he became very friendly with Chopin but spent much of his life in seclusion.

GRANDMOTHER'S SONG

VOLKMANN, Op.27 No.10

Greatly influenced by Schumann, Robert Volkmann composed much orchestral and chamber music, and taught in Prague, Vienna and Budapest. The collection of *Grandmother's songs* from which this comes was published in 1880.

LESSON in A

STERNDALE BENNETT, Op.33 No.7

A close friend of Schumann and Mendelssohn, Sheffield-born Sterndale Bennett founded the Bach Choir, was for ten years conductor of the Philharmonic Society, and in 1866 became principal of the Royal Academy of Music, where he himself had been a student. His Op.33 consists of 30 pieces in all the keys.

GRANDMAMA TELLS A GHOST STORY

KULLAK, Op.81 No.3

Theodor Kullak, one of a family of musicians, was a pupil of Czerny and became court pianist to the King of Prussia. He was a co-founder of a conservatory in Berlin in 1850, but, falling out with his partner, he set up a school of his own (also in Berlin) five years later.

STUDY in D

LOESCHHORN, Op.65 No.18

A distinguished Berlin piano teacher (awarded the title Royal Professor in 1858), Albert Loeschhorn also, for many years, organised a highly successful series of chamber concerts. He wrote a large number of studies for the piano, among them his Op.65 collection, which became standard educational works.

A SERIOUS MOMENT

GURLITT, Op.210 No.27

A main influence on Cornelius Gurlitt was Schumann, whom he visited with his friend Carl Reinecke (the son of his teacher). Altona, where Gurlitt was born, was then Danish: after teaching in Copenhagen he became a professor at the Hamburg Conservatory. The present piece comes from his album entitled *Der erste Vortrag* ('First pieces to play').

OLD CHRISTMAS CAROL

FRANCK

César Franck exercised a powerful influence on a whole generation of French musicians: among his many pupils to become famous were Chausson, Duparc and d'Indy. The present piece comes from *L'Organiste*, a collection of 59 pieces for harmonium written at the extreme end of his life and published only in 1896, after his death.

AB 1899

MINIATURE

KIRCHNER, Op.62 No.6

One of Schumann's most gifted followers, Theodor Kirchner was successively an organist and conductor in Switzerland for 30 years, director of a music school in Würzburg, a teacher in Leipzig and a professor of chamber music in Dresden.

AB 1899

THE ECHO

REINECKE, Op.206 No.21

After initial successes as a violinist, Carl Reinecke had a distinguished career as a pianist, conductor and composer. He was in turn court pianist in Copenhagen, a professor of music in Cologne, director of music in Breslau, for 35 years conductor of the Leipzig Gewandhaus and simultaneously, for even longer, taught at the Leipzig Conservatory. This piece is the first movement of a 'Pastoral Sonatina'.

AB 1899

ALLEGRETTO

ROHDE, Op.80 No.1

Eduard Rohde was born in Halle and became an organist and teacher in Berlin. His voluminous output consisted largely – apart from his piano pieces – of songs, folksong arrangements and motets. This *Allegretto* is the first of his six *Gefällige Clavierstücke* ('Agreeable piano pieces') of 1870.

MARCH OF THE WOODEN SOLDIERS

Moderato [♩ = c.120]

TCHAIKOVSKY, Op.39 No.5

Tchaikovsky's Op.39 *Children's album* was written in the country near Kiev 'as a relaxation', according to the composer, after completing his Fourth Symphony and the opera *Evgeny Onyegin*.

INNOCENT FRANKNESS

CUI, Op.20 No.1

Like other members of the 'mighty handful' of Russian nationalist composers, Cui originally pursued music only as a sideline: he was a lecturer in the School of Military Engineering in St Petersburg, and an expert on fortifications. Later he became a trenchant and witty music critic. Several of his Op.20 *Miniatures* were afterwards arranged for orchestra.

LAST SATURDAY EVENING

GRIEG, Op.17 No.15

After studying in Leipzig, and with Gade in Copenhagen, Grieg returned to Norway, where his interest was aroused by his native folk music. The present piece is in a set of *Norwegian folksongs and dances* (arrangements of tunes collected by the eminent folk-music pioneer, Ludvig Lindeman) that he published in 1869, soon after founding a Norwegian Academy of Music.

AB 1899

SCHERZO

Moderato [♩ = 76]

H. HOFMANN, Op.77 No.7

Heinrich Hofmann was a Berlin pianist and teacher who had considerable success in Germany with his orchestral works and operas. This piece comes from a volume of *Skizzen* ('Sketches').

PROUD HORSEMAN

R. FUCHS, Op.47 No.2

Robert Fuchs, best known for his clarinet quintet and his fine Serenades for string orchestra, was an influential professor at the Vienna Conservatory, of which his elder brother later became director. Among his pupils were Mahler and Hugo Wolf. This piece comes from his *Jugendalbum* ('Album for the young').

FIRST SORROW

GODARD, Op.149 No.6

Much influenced by Schumann (whose *Kinderscenen* he orchestrated), Benjamin Godard was a French viola player who had been an infant prodigy in composition. He had an elegant lyrical gift, but his works – including eight operas, three concertos and five symphonies – have all faded into oblivion except for a *Berceuse* in his 1885 opera *Jocelyn*.

AB 1899

BALL GAME

KRUG, Op.107 No.4

A pupil of Cornelius Gurlitt in his native city of Hamburg, and then studying in Leipzig, Arnold Krug taught in Berlin for five years, and then, after visiting France and Italy thanks to a scholarship, returned to Hamburg, where he organised a choral society and became a professor at the Conservatory. He wrote a number of choral, orchestral and chamber works.

SPRINGTIME AND YOUTH

Andante [♩ = 88]

FIBICH

Although Czech by birth and residence, Fibich received his musical education in Leipzig, Paris and Mannheim, so that his music is generally less nationalistic than that of his older compatriots Smetana and Dvořák. For a time he was a conductor at the National Theatre in Prague. The present piece was written in 1865.

A TALE

SCHARWENKA, Op.62 No.3

Lento e mesto [♩ = 92]

The younger and more enterprising of two musical brothers, Xaver Scharwenka toured extensively as a pianist, gaining a great reputation as a Chopin interpreter, and founded no fewer than three music schools – two, in 1881 and 1914, in Berlin, one in New York in 1891. His Op.62 *Album für die Jugend* ('Album for the young') was published in the early 1880s.

ARABESQUE

KARGANOV, Op.6 No.2

Génari Karganov, a Georgian, wrote a large number of small piano pieces, mostly for younger players; but, like Schubert, he died before reaching the age of 32.

ALLEGRETTO SCHERZANDO

LYAPUNOV

As a member of the Imperial Geographic Society, Lyapunov (who had studied with Tchaikovsky) collected and published nearly 300 folksongs from Russian provinces. After being assistant director of the Imperial Choir in St Petersburg and an inspector of music, he became a colleague of Maikapar on the staff of the Conservatory there; but after the Revolution he settled in Paris.

VALSE MINIATURE

REBIKOV, Op.10 No.10

Vladimir Rebikov, who had studied in Moscow, Berlin and Vienna, founded musical societies in Odessa and Kishinev (Bessarabia). In 1901 he settled in Moscow, where his style, previously much influenced by Tchaikovsky, underwent a radical change, so that he became one of the most 'advanced' Russian composers of his day.

A PASSING THOUGHT

MAIKAPAR, Op.4 No.1

For 20 years a professor at the St Petersburg Conservatory, where he himself had been a student, Samuil Maikapar had also been a pupil of the great piano teacher Leschetizky in Vienna. He wrote a large number of small pieces for the piano as well as studies for special aspects of piano technique.

THE EVENING BELL

GRANADOS

Besides his *Danzas españolas* and *Goyescas* (his finest piano work), Granados wrote several albums of picturesque short keyboard pieces, some while still a student at the Madrid Conservatory. This is the fourth piece in his *Bocetos* ('Sketches').

AB 1899

CATCH-ME-IF-YOU-CAN

REGER, Op.17 No.2

Max Reger, an enormously productive composer in almost every sphere except opera, held important teaching posts in Munich and Leipzig. His Op.17 suite *Aus der Jugendzeit* ('From youthful days') was written shortly after completing his studies in Wiesbaden.

JUMPING JACK

NIELSEN, Op.11 No.4

Nielsen's *Humoresque-Bagatelles*, from which this is taken, were written in 1897, while he was still a violinist in the orchestra of the Theatre Royal, Copenhagen. He subsequently became, for some years, conductor of the Royal Opera and of the Copenhagen Musical Society, and for a time director of the Conservatory there.

MARCH

GEDIKE, Op.36 No.29

A fourth-generation member of a family of composers of German extraction, Alexander Gedike studied under Arensky in Moscow. He won the Rubinstein Prize in an international competition for composers in Vienna; wrote four operas to his own libretti, four concertos and three symphonies, as well as much piano music; and was also a professor of the piano and organ at the Moscow Conservatory.

AQUARELLE

GLIÈRE, Op.34 No.17

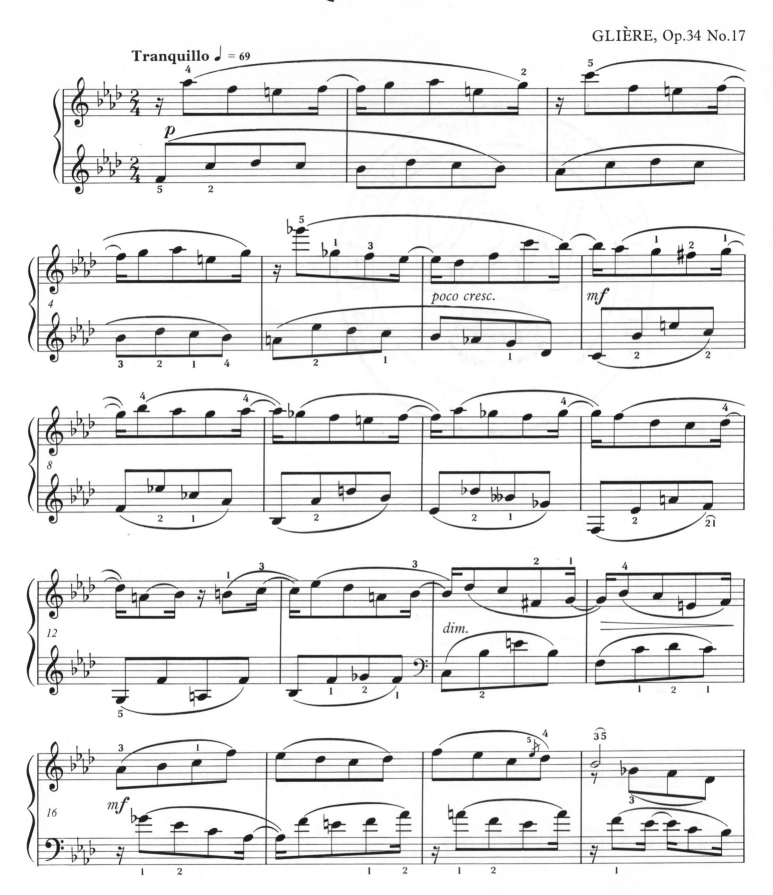

A pupil of Arensky, and himself the teacher of Prokofiev, Glière was active at the Conservatories of Moscow and of Kiev (where for six years he was director). He made valuable contributions to research into the folk music of the southern Soviet republics. This *Aquarelle* comes from his *24 Pièces caractéristiques*.

AB 1899

CLOWNING

KABALEVSKY, Op.27 No.10

Though he has to his credit five operas, four symphonies and six concertos (three of them for young players), Kabalevsky is best known for his work in the educational field. After being appointed a professor at the Moscow Conservatory, he became head of a commission on the musical education of children and, later, president of the International Society for Musical Education.

STUDY in D

DUNHILL, Op.74 Bk.II No.6

Andantino espressivo [♩ = 69]

After studying with Stanford, Thomas Dunhill was, for ten years, a music master at Eton and, for much longer, a professor at the Royal College of Music. His breadth of taste enabled him to write distinguished chamber works and, at the other end of the musical spectrum, the very successful light opera *Tantivy Towers*.

AB 1899